Andre's Wild Ride

Nestor Xouris
artist

Jackson Mauzé
author

André Kajlich
athlete

Maria Durana
book design

Mountains & Awesome people
of Telluride,

Luv Ppl Luv Nature
1 Be Awesome, Enjoy the ride

To my son David,
for taking life to new heights in the face of cancer.

This dedication was written by one of the book's sponsors for her son.
This story wouldn't exist without a ton of support like hers, or without
many good friends like him.

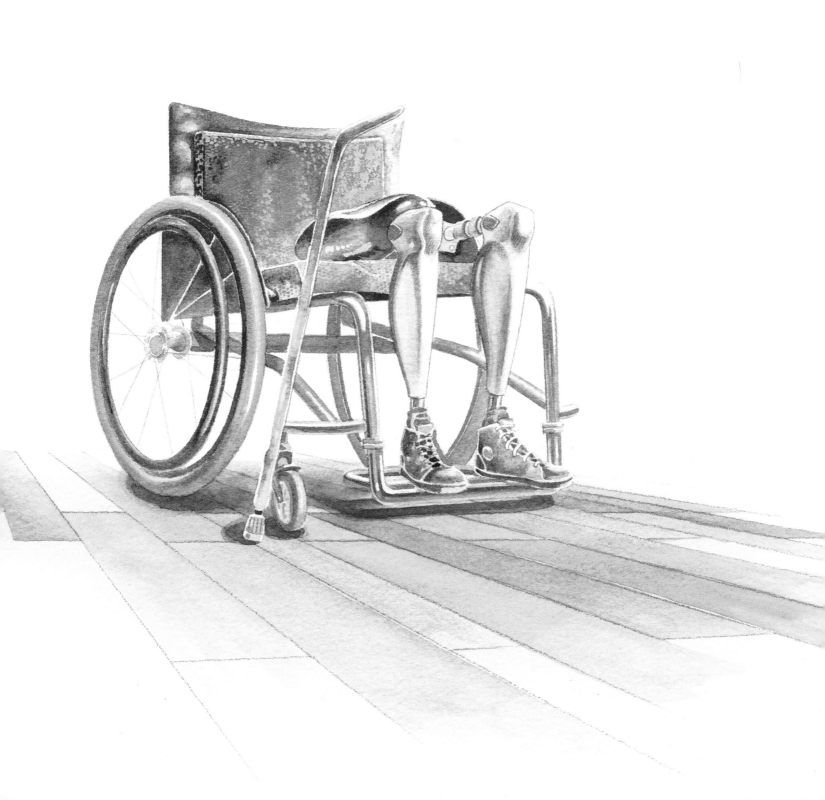

Hi! My name is André.

It's nice to meet you.

These are my metal legs,
my cane, and my wheelchair.

I lost my legs in a train accident
so I need these to get around
sometimes.

But mostly, I like to get around
on my bike.

And this is the story of my
longest ride yet!

André waved goodbye to the California surf in sunny San Diego. The longest race of his life was about to begin.

Through the earpiece in his helmet, he could hear
his friends as his mind drifted to the past year.

You trained every day for this.
Even when you were tired.
Even when it was Christmas!

André did not reply.
He did not need to.

The race began with a BANG!

André was off.

The road melted away beneath his handcycle and San Diego faded quickly into the distance.

André crested his first mountain. The land stretched out below. A beautiful sight, but ohhhhhhhh...

how far he had to go.

In the Arizona desert, the race began to heat up.

It's not so bad! Only 109 degrees.

The hot sun scowled overhead,
    scorching his face, and cracking his lips.

Only 1,000 miles in and the race was taking a toll.

But he pushed on.

In Colorado,
André began to climb
the biggest mountain
he'd ever seen.

Or maybe it just
felt that way.

As the air grew thin
and day turned
to night...

The temperature plummeted.

André shook and shivered.

But now more than ever was no time to stop, because his only chance to stay warm was to just keep pedaling.

André survived the frigid night and as the sun rose, he relaxed on the downhills.

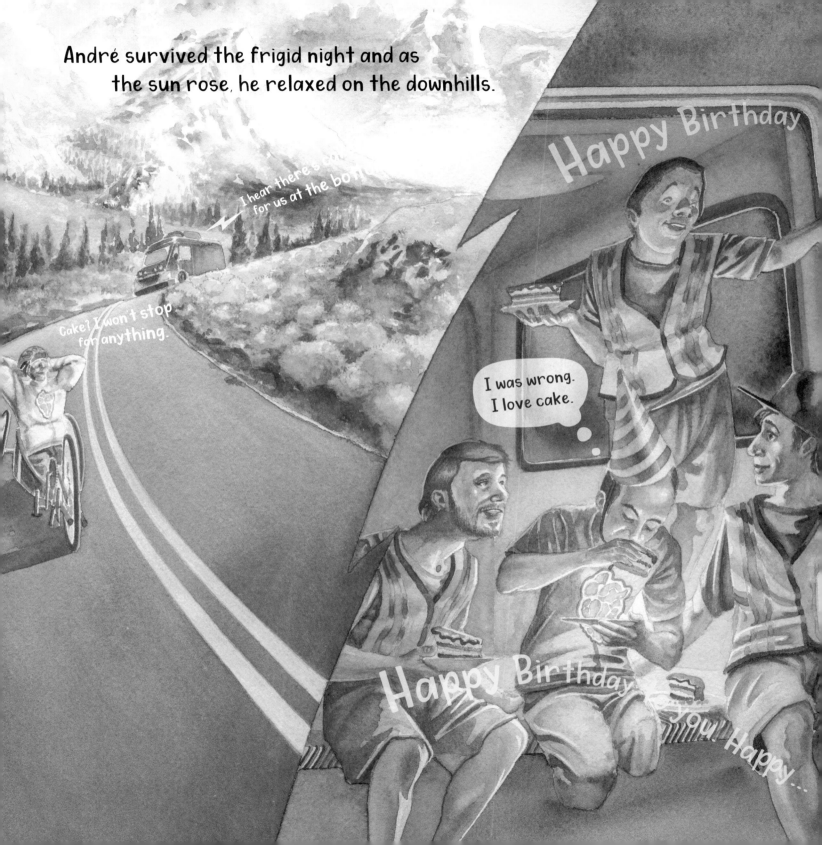

...where a **whipping** wind can send a rider sailing down the road.

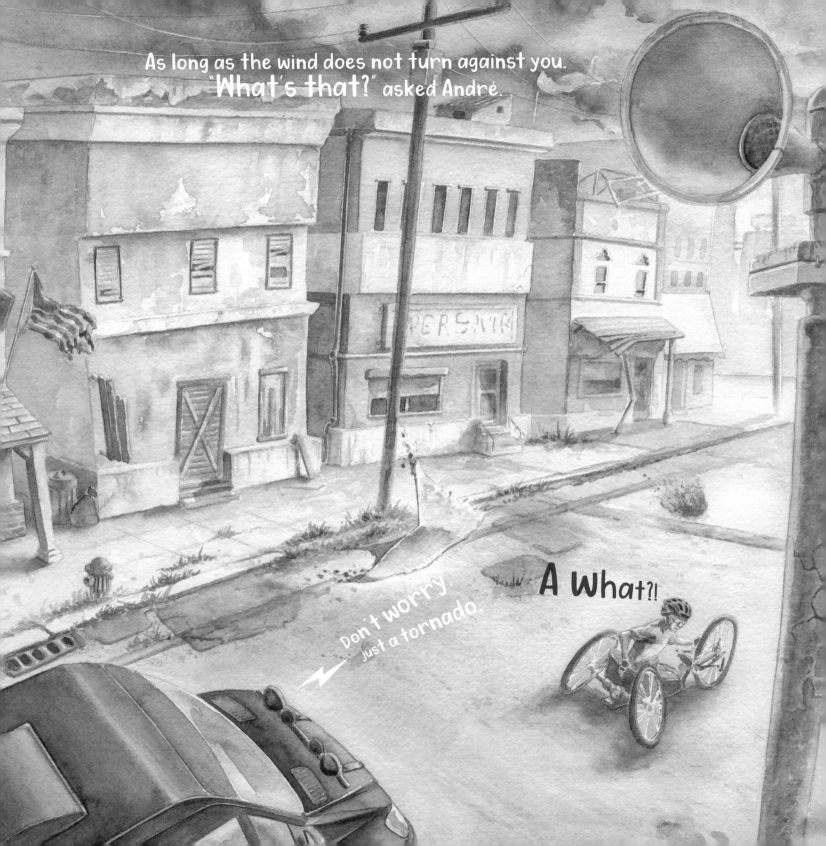

They dodged many tornados but not the
storm brewing ahead.

I see a tunnel
and it looks angry!

André!
Those are clouds.

The storm hit **HARD**, flooding the roads.

In Virginia, the road twisted up the Smokey Mountains like crumbling snakes. This was the last challenge between André and the finish line.

His muscles burned and his bones ached.

Everything seemed to be saying, "**QUIT!**"

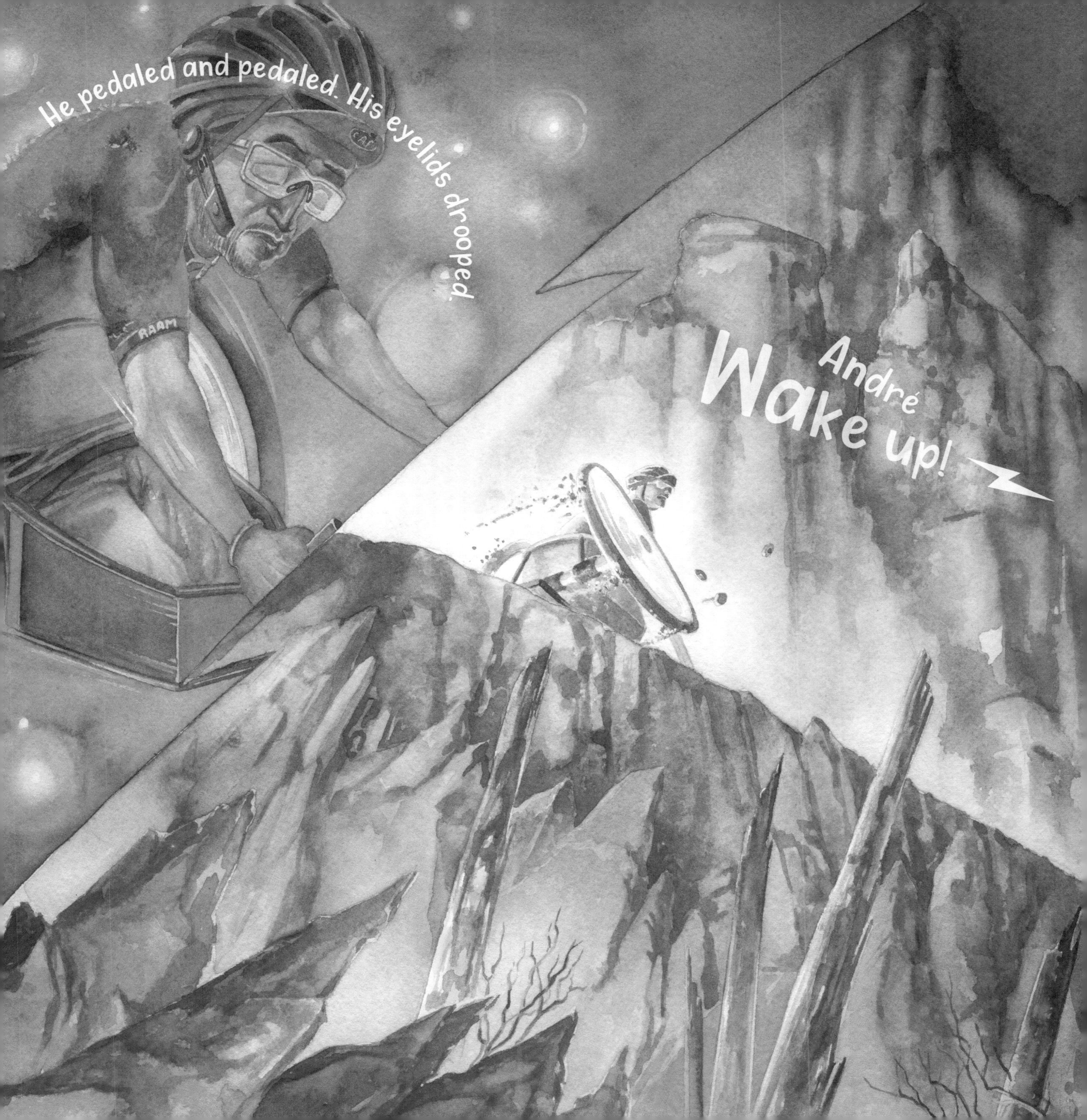
He pedaled and pedaled. His eyelids drooped.
André
Wake up!

Through the fog in his mind, an owl swooped down next to him.
You want to give up?
I think I...

Now's not the time to think. It's time to do!

André *blinked* and the owl was gone.

He was pedaling up a hill and next to him
was a friend from the van.

André had been biking for 22 hours every day for over 10 days. He had wanted to quit...

but pushed on...

...Something MAGICAL. It proved that he could do anything. For André, this was just the beginning.

And the next morning, he crossed the finish line!

After 12 days and 16 hours, he became the first person to Race Across America on a handcyle.

But his mind continued to pedal away in search of new adventures.

Easy? Ha!
Good one.
Maybe, I'll write a children's book. That sounds easy...

About André Kajlich

After losing both legs in a subway accident in the Czech Republic, André took hard won wisdoms and became an ultra endurance pioneer.

He's held a #1 World Ranking as a paratriathlete, was Ironman World Champion, and is the first and only wheelchair athlete to finish the Hawaii Ultraman Triathlon and many other ultras.

Follow along André's latest project. | @andrekajlich | www.andrekajlich.com

---

NO LEGS. ALL HEART.

Race Across America

Another first, and the subject of this book, was his completion of the Race Across America (RAAM) in 2017, handcycling 3,100 miles in just 12 days, sleeping 90 minutes a night to make it from Oceanside, CA to Annapolis, MD.

He is the subject of the documentary film **NO LEGS. ALL HEART.** | www.nolegsallheart.com

---

What's Next?

After crossing South America with two teammates, that also have disabilities, André, Mohamed, and Lucas founded the Lowest Highest Foundation to raise awareness and improve the lives of people with disabilities, focused on improving attitudes and addressing the lack of services in developing countries.

Learn more. | @lowesthighest | www.lowesthighest.org

If this book inspired you, please consider supporting the Challenged Athletes Foundation, they have helped many people with disabilities become active - including André!

www.challengedathletes.org

Printed in China